Revised and enlarged edition by

WILLIAM R. VAN DERSAL

The land renewed

The story of soil conservation

HENRY Z. WALCK, INC. / NEW YORK 1968

The illustrations in this book were made from photographs supplied for the most part by the United States Soil Conservation Service. The picture opposite page 10 was furnished by the United States Forest Service; that opposite page 22 came from the New York Port Authority. To these agencies I am glad to offer my sincere appreciation for their very material assistance in making this book possible.

W. R. V.

The original edition of *The Land Renewed* appeared in 1946. My close friend and associate, Edward H. Graham, and I wrote it together. Twenty-two years of progress in the conservation of soil, water, and other natural resources has made it necessary to change this new edition a good deal. Even so, it is based on the original work.

Dr. Graham and I agreed several years ago that the book should be revised. However, he could not participate because of the press of a number of other activities in which he was then engaged. We decided, therefore, that I should proceed with this new edition.

In May of 1966 my friend passed away suddenly and unexpectedly. His very substantial contributions to our knowledge in the field of natural resources will remain a monument to his efforts. His thinking and philosophy will unquestionably play an important and significant part in the development of natural resource conservation throughout the world for a great many years to come.

It is appropriate therefore that this book be dedicated

TO EDWARD H. GRAHAM
one of the world's great conservationists

Contents

In the beginning

It is nearly a thousand years since the first European explorers reached this land we now live in. It is almost as long since Leif Ericson and his band of Norsemen landed somewhere on the New England coast. Five hundred years after Leif Ericson, the New World was rediscovered by Christopher Columbus. The reports Columbus took back inspired many people to cross the Atlantic. Real settlement began nearly four centuries ago.

America was a wilderness when the early settlers arrived. The eastern shores supported an almost continuous forest of hardwoods and pines, which covered the Appalachian mountain system and surrounded the Great Lakes. Westward it gave way to stretches of treeless grassland. In the Southwest, giant cactus and thorny shrubs dominated the deserts. To the north, pine- and fir-clad ranges of the Rocky Mountains alternated with dry basins covered with sagebrush. West toward the Pacific, conifer forests clothed the Sierra Nevadas and Cascades. In this wilderness lived a million Indians and innumerable buffalo, antelope, elk, wolves, bears and panthers. Overhead flew passenger pigeons, waterfowl, and countless other birds.

Today this magnificent wilderness is nearly gone. Once the land was free to anyone who wanted it, but now every acre belongs to someone, or to the government. Our country has become a varied pattern of farms and ranches, cities and towns, railroads and highways. It is a wealthy country, and we who live in it have one of the highest standards of living in the world. This is because of our land. The land is the key to the power and freedom and well-being of our nation.

Scenes like this greeted early explorers in America

Primeval forests of the East

The pioneers settling our eastern shores were on the edge of a vast, magnificent forest, which stretched from Maine to Florida, covering nearly all the land from the seacoast to Illinois. There it split into two great arms, one extending north and west to the edge of North Dakota, the other spreading south and west to the center of Texas.

The trees in this wilderness were giants. Some reached heights of 100 to 250 feet and were as much as 10 or 15 feet in diameter. The floor of the forest was strewn with fallen trees and rotten branches and covered with a thick layer of decaying vegetation. Thousands of years of growth and decay built a lush soil of remarkable fertility, which was capable of holding water as a sponge does. Great swamps existed where none are known today.

In the South, slash, loblolly, and longleaf pine dominated the drier lands. Magnolias, cypress, and live oaks grew in the wetter places. In the central East, there were many varieties of oaks, hickories, tulip-poplars, gums, and chestnuts. Northward beech, birch, hemlock, and sugar maple were commonest, with walnuts, ash, and gigantic sycamores in the lowlands. Far in the North and in the high mountains, white pine, red pine, jack pine, spruce, and balsam fir were most common.

The Indians made clearings in this forest where they grew corn, squashes, beans, and, in the South, melons and tobacco.

For the most part the settlers found this magnificent forest an obstacle to be overcome. They set about destroying it to get at the rich lands they needed for growing food.

Primeval forest of the eastern United States — an existing remnant

Plains and prairies

Eastward the forest gave way to grassland. The seas of tall waving grasses on its eastern edges, which sparkled with flowers in the spring, were called prairies. They were found in various parts of Ohio, Indiana, Illinois, and nearby states.

As explorers went westward, they found that halfway across the Dakotas, and more or less in a line with this southward, the prairies changed. East of this line (about the 100th meridian) the grasses were usually tall. West of the line, clear to the Rocky Mountains, the grasses were short. This short-grass country is what we mean when we speak of the Great Plains. It used to be called the Great American Desert. In dry years the grass was very short indeed, and in wetter years it was lush but still short.

Some 140,000 Indians existed on the Great Plains, living mainly on the Plains buffalo. Grama grasses, buffalo grass, and, in the wetter places, Indian grass grew here. Cactus flourished and competed with the grasses. Only little draws and stream banks supported willows and perhaps cottonwood trees. Possibly sixty million buffalo ranged on these grasslands, and countless elk and antelope grazed. There were also wolves and, in the North, the giant, flesh-eating grizzly bears.

Some people thought the Great Plains was a lush grass country, while others thought it was a desert. It turns out they were both right. We know now that the climate shifts in this vast interior area. There are dry seasons followed by wet ones—and no one can tell when it will be dry or wet. It has taken us many years to learn how to live on the Plains.

An expanse of grama grass in the Plains may have looked like this in the early days

Buffalo on the Wichita Refuge

The Far West

The western third of our country contains great basins and valleys interspersed with mountains and high plateaus. It is a land of great variety and great beauty.

In the Southwest there is a true desert. A sparse cover of cactus, creosote bush, ocotillo, mesquite, and other thorny, wiry shrubs is spread over vast areas of sand and rock. The landscape is colored primarily by the rocks, gravel, and sand, but if it rains, a host of tiny plants suddenly sprout from long-dormant seeds, and the desert appears to bloom.

In the high mountains the varieties of trees change from north to south. In Idaho and Montana, ponderosa pine, western white pine, spruces, firs, and aspens are common. Southward they gradually give way to oaks, junipers, and pinyon pines.

There are endless stretches of sagebrush between the Rockies and the Sierras and Cascades of the Far West. This gray-white shrub, characteristic of arid country, supported the famous sage grouse. Here also ranged antelope, mule deer, and elk.

Along the Pacific Coast great valleys separated mountain chains. In the North and in the mountains grew the colossal sequoias, the Douglas firs, Sitka spruce, western hemlock, arbor-vitae, and sugar pines. Mosses in mats a foot thick grew on the forest floor and clothed the lower limbs of many trees.

The southern coastal areas were dry but the Pacific Northwest had plenty of rain. Although the western mountains were barriers to settlement, there were some wonderful locations for farming in the inter-mountain valleys.

Trees like these sequoias—largest in the world —were found by early explorers in California

People change the land

Very little wilderness is left in the eastern part of our country, but in the West there are still some fair-sized areas that we believe are very much as they were in early times. As the settlers increased, they cut and burned the great forests, destroying timber of immense value. The brush was grubbed out, and the settlers planted corn and wheat and orchards. In the prairies the tall grasses were plowed under. Eventually the prairies became one of our richest agricultural areas—the Cornbelt.

The wet areas were drained and ditches were cut to carry off the water. Some excellent agricultural land resulted, but some areas had later to be abandoned as useless. The very dry areas, especially in the Southwest, needed water to produce crops, so streams were diverted and storage ponds were built.

Wheat was grown in the Great Plains. In good years it did well, but in dry years the crops failed and the plowed soil began to blow. Too many cattle and sheep were put on the grassland for it to support in dry years. In many ways the Plains were badly abused.

Many forests of the West were also cut. The western valleys, once irrigated, proved wonderfully fertile, and oranges and lemons, grapefruit, dates, and other such fruits began to be grown in the southern valleys.

Our forefathers, in reshaping the wilderness, were beginning to establish an agricultural nation and to prepare the base for the great agricultural miracle of the present day.

Early settlers clearing land; photographed in 1880

The land changes people

During the time America was being settled, most people lived on farms. Just about everything they ate and wore came from the land. Although today more people live in cities and towns than live on the land, our food still comes from the soil and so do most of the things we wear.

The food we get is only as good as the soil it comes from. It makes no difference whether we eat corn directly from the soil, or milk from cows that feed on corn. If the soil is rich and fertile, the food is filled with health-giving elements of value in our diets. If the soil is poor, so is the food it produces. Our soil is exactly as important to us as the food we eat.

Not only do we get most of our food from the land, but in one sense we also get our freedom from it. When people have all the free land they want, as we did for four centuries, they become independent. Any time they want to, they can have another chance to build a new life on new land. When people are as free as that, they come to love liberty all the more. They will fight anything that threatens their freedom, and they will choose a form of government that makes their liberty secure—just as we did. That is why we say that freedom in America was nourished and sustained by the land itself.

Within our boundaries we have almost two billion acres of land. We do not yet know how much our land could produce if every bit of it were used exactly right. But we do know that this great expanse of land is the key to the power and the freedom of our nation.

Symbol of a new nation and a new people

Cities on the land

To begin with, as we have already noted, nearly everyone lived on the land. Gradually people began to live in clusters and villages and small towns evolved. Some of these grew into cities, and most of the biggest developed where land met water.

Some of our cities have become very large. For example, in 1966, New York City had nearly eight million people in the city proper, more than fourteen million in its general metropolitan area. This is our biggest city.

Our cities are now enlarging in another way. Not only do they have more people in them, but they are spreading out to cover more land. Suburbs around all our cities spread far out into the country and continue to spread. Our cities covered an area of seventeen million acres in 1950, and we suspect that they may cover an area of forty-one million acres by the year 2000.

Villages and towns and small cities are strung out along the principal highways, which connect them with the really big metropolitan centers. Soon the whole complex becomes city. We are developing a number of these—for example, the one between Boston, New York, Philadelphia, Baltimore, and Washington, D.C., or between San Francisco and Los Angeles.

Land for cities is very important and, of course, very valuable. Today two thirds of all the people in America live in cities, and when people live in a city, they may not see or realize the tremendously important relationship between land and the production of food and may fail to understand why conservation is of such vital importance to our standard of living.

LAND TROUBLES

Topsoil

A good fertile soil takes a long time to form under natural conditions. Part of it comes from rock that is weathered by sun, wind, rain, and frost, and part from dead leaves, and other dead parts of plants as well as animals. Bacteria and molds grow in the soil and change it in many ways. Many kinds of animals, from microscopic worms to earthworms, moles, and other burrowing animals help to mix and loosen it.

The valuable and important part of most soils is the surface layer. If you dig into the earth you can see this surface layer in profile. In the picture it is the dark layer just under the grasses growing on top of it. This is usually called topsoil. It is richest in the chemical elements that plants must have to grow and has most of the minerals they need.

The surface soil, or topsoil, blends gradually into the next layer below it, the subsoil, which usually has few plant roots as it contains less food in a form the plants can use. In the picture this particular subsoil is lighter in color.

Soil profiles are not alike everywhere. In the prairies topsoil is deep, sometimes several feet thick, but in forests it may be only a few inches thick. In some soils deposited by wind action there may be no clearcut separation between topsoil and subsoil. Soils that have the deepest surface layer are likely to be naturally the most fertile.

Soils formed in nature are not always the best for crop plants, and we may need to add various minerals or other substances to make them what we want. Even so, the most valuable of all our natural resources is the topsoil of our lands.

Topsoil—the world's most valuable resource
(The surveyor's rod is marked in tenths of a foot)

Humus and soil

Scattered about on the top of the ground you can see all sorts of leaves, twigs, dead insects and pieces of dead plants as well as animals. These remains are gradually rotting and becoming mixed with the topsoil. Eventually—and you can see this by digging into the earth a bit—this material cannot be recognized at all. It has become part of the soil itself.

All such dead plant and animal debris goes to form a dark-colored material known as humus. We do not know exactly what this is. Since it comes from living material it must contain chemical elements necessary to life. Chemists cannot yet give us a clearcut chemical formula for each of the complex chemical substances it contains. Humus is exceedingly important and soil with plenty of it will grow things well.

Humus contains food elements that living plants can absorb and use, and in this sense acts as a fertilizer. It also acts to make the soil loose and crumbly so that plant roots can easily grow through it. It changes the soil so that water can trickle into it easily, and humus-filled soil can hold much more water than a soil lacking humus.

Soil conservationists learned long ago that humus would help to keep the soil from washing away under heavy rains. That is why many soil conservation measures are aimed at getting more humus into the soil.

If people realized the value of humus they would not burn dead leaves in the fall, for these decay readily and form humus which can improve our garden soils. Gardeners, no less than conservationists, value materials that some people throw away.

Water erosion

The early settlers did not think topsoil was valuable. If they were not satisfied with the crops they could grow in one place, they moved elsewhere. Now there is no more free land and we have to use the land we have in the best way we know.

When rain falls on bare soil, it washes the topmost particles away and runs off as muddy water. Muddy water carries soil, and the faster it runs the more soil it can carry. When it slows down, it begins to drop soil, and when it stops running altogether, after a while the mud settles out.

This simple process is known as erosion. When it takes place on a big scale, hundreds of thousands of tons of soil may be washed away in a single rainstorm. The topsoil is always the first to go.

Erosion is not always easy to recognize. The picture shows a bean field on the side of a hill. The very top of the hill has a good cover of shrubs and grasses so that the rain disturbs it very little. But not far below the top of the field, running water has carried away first a little and then a lot of soil. As the water ran down the hill it went faster, picking up soil as it went, and making deep cuts in the fields. In a few years this field will be worn out because the few inches of precious topsoil will be gone for good.

Sometimes, instead of making little rills and cuts in the soil, the water washes downhill in a thin, wide sheet. As this sheet of muddy water flows evenly downhill, it removes a very thin layer of the surface soil. The effect is the same—the soil washes off the land and ends up downstream somewhere.

Erosion carries away the topsoil

Little gullies

On large fields that are bare, rain water may carry off the soil in great sheets. This is called sheet erosion. But where the muddy water runs in little channels, it cuts the channels deeper. Sometimes the water spills over from a high place to make a muddy waterfall. It is at this point that a gully forms. As the water pours over the falls, it tears out the soil behind it and with each rain the waterfall cuts back farther.

In the top picture you can see one of these gullies forming. The rain water ran across this field, carrying soil with it, until it finally reached the lowest point. There it spilled over into a ditch along the road. In the bottom picture you can see the gully three months later. In that short time it cut back fifteen feet into the field. It took out more fence posts and tons of both topsoil and subsoil.

If nothing is done to stop the water, this gully will keep on eating back into the field, which is used for corn. The soil is very rich, but at the rate the gully is forming (and sheet erosion is going on too), it will not be very many years before the field is wasted land. The gully will fork and get deeper, and farm equipment will not be able to cross it.

The man who owned the land did not notice the gully at first. Perhaps if he had known what was going to happen in only a few years, he would have done something about it.

Little gullies like this are still all too common in our country. Wherever they appear, they are a sure indication that the farmer or owner is misusing his land. We cannot afford losses of land such as this.

Gullies grow with land misuse

Big gullies

This is not the Grand Canyon. It is a giant gully that used to be no larger than the one shown on the page before. Now it is 150 feet deep and getting deeper. It was formed by rain water cutting through the soil—that is, erosion. And it is only seventy or eighty years since the gully began.

The water has cut through the topsoil, through the subsoil, and deep below. As the water flows along the bottom of the gully, it cuts into the side walls and more masses of earth fall in. Roads, houses, fields, everything goes into this gully as it eats its way along.

Certainly the earliest settlers never dreamed that land could be destroyed like this. George Washington knew about erosion and so did Thomas Jefferson. These men and many others often warned that erosion was dangerous.

Some soils, of course, erode more easily than others. Also, the harder it rains and the steeper the land slopes are, the more chance there is for erosion to occur. Erosion can be serious almost anywhere in our country, and a little more than half the land in America is susceptible to erosion. The hazards of erosion are especially serious in the Southeast, where the erosion is caused by water. In the Plains erosion by wind is a potential danger.

Many millions of acres of American land, once used for growing crops, have been so severely eroded that they can no longer be cultivated, and many more millions of acres have been very seriously damaged. We are engaged now in restoring such lands.

Erosion can destroy land wholesale

Sediment

The muddy water that runs off the land has to go somewhere. If it spreads out over the fields in the lowlands and slows down, it drops its load of soil. As time goes on, the soil it drops gets poorer because the supply of topsoil up the hill is beginning to run out, and the good topsoil of the fields below is finally covered with subsoil from the fields above.

If the muddy water flows into streams and rivers, the rivers turn muddy after every rain. They are full of sediment—the name for soil particles carried in water. There is very poor fishing in rivers full of sediment. You cannot drink water full of it, nor can you use such water in mills and factories. Wherever the river flows more slowly, the sediment settles to the bottom and fills up the river bed. These beds of sediment make the river change its course and make floods worse. Sediment also collects in reservoirs, making them useless.

The picture shows a dam built in 1904. The water it stored was to be used for water power, but by 1915 the reservoir was useless. In eleven years four fifths of the lake was filled with sediment. There was only room for the river to get through. Many of our reservoirs are filling with sediment.

Sediment goes down the river and piles up at its mouth where the water slows its pace as it enters the sea. Oysters and clams cannot live there, mud flats and deltas build up, and beds of sediment make it harder for boats to use the stream.

A river carrying a heavy load of sediment is polluted. Erosion sediment is one of the most important and commonest sources of pollution.

Floods

As great loads of sediment pour into our rivers, the beds of the streams become clogged, and the streams are forced out of their channels in some places. They cut into the fields they flow through, eating into rich bottom land that should be producing food.

But they do much worse. Far upstream, the protecting cover of grass or trees or other plants has been cleared for farming. This lets the water run off faster. On the open fields, as the topsoil gets thinner, the water runs still faster, because good topsoil can soak up a great deal of water but the subsoil does this much more slowly. The faster the water runs off, after heavy rains, the more there is in the streams. Soon the riverbeds are not large enough to carry all the water, the rivers pour over their banks, and we have a flood.

Floods cause tremendous damage. Human lives are lost, homes are destroyed, and roads are washed out. Villages, towns, and whole cities are flooded, water supplies fail, electricity is cut off and railroads are wrecked.

There have always been floods but the floods we have now are much worse because erosion makes them so. Though the damage along the rivers is terrible, it is only part of the story. Topsoil, source of all our food, is on its way to the sea.

We may never be able to stop all floods, but we do know how to prevent the smaller ones and how to cut down the size of the larger ones. We have to start where the floodwaters start—far up in the headwaters of the little streams, on the land itself.

Floods are more common because of erosion upstream

Wind erosion

Just as water can pick up soil and carry it away, so wind can blow soil up into the air. When a brisk wind sweeps across dry, bare soil, it begins to pick up dust. The faster the wind blows, the more soil and the bigger the particles it can carry. When the wind dies down, the dust gradually settles. Biggest particles fall out first, finer particles later.

When very strong dry winds blow over great areas of exposed soil, gigantic clouds of dust may be swept up into the air to form dust storms. They may cause severe damage, especially in very dry years when the soil blows easily. Soil from the central part of America has been known to blow as far east as Washington, D.C., and out into the Atlantic Ocean. Millions of tons of soil may blow hundreds or even thousands of miles.

When the dust storm is in full swing, it may not be possible to see more than a few yards. Clothing and food get full of dirt, and dust gets into everything. Automobiles may have to stop traveling because drivers cannot see ahead, and airplanes must fly high to keep above the dark clouds of blowing soil. In storms like these breathing is difficult, and people may get "dust pneumonia."

As with water erosion, the best soil—topsoil—is always the first to go with the wind. Several inches can be removed during a few hours of strong, steady wind action. As wind erosion goes on, the topsoil gets thinner and the land becomes poorer. Some ten million acres of land in the United States have been seriously worn by wind erosion alone, and a much larger area has been partly damaged.

Fields fill up with sand dunes

Homesteads are covered up

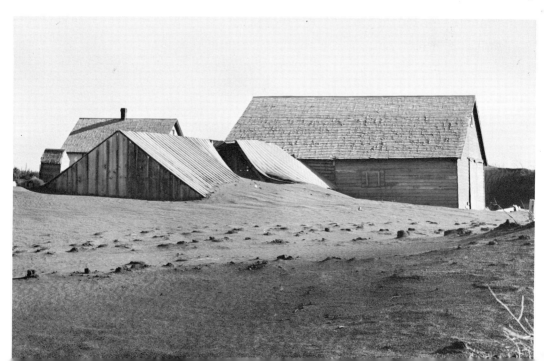

The Dust Bowl

During and after the First World War, a great deal of land in the Plains was plowed up and sown to wheat. Prices were high; we needed wheat; and there had been good rains for several years. Most of the land was grassland where buffalo used to graze, and later cattle. But the rains did not keep coming, the wheat failed, and finally the soil lay bare. In 1933 and 1934 the winds that always blew strong and hard across the level Plains began lifting the dry soil and carrying it off.

In the High Plains around the panhandles of Texas and Oklahoma—the Dust Bowl—things were very bad. Dust clouds swept off this vast area and blew across two thirds of the United States. People were shocked to realize that this dust settling on them was *soil* from the Great Plains.

One storm, in May of 1934, moved some 300 million tons of soil off the land, and dropped about 100 tons of it per square mile in its path eastward. In the Dust Bowl itself dust piled in on homes and drifted like snow in great banks along the fence rows.

The Dust Bowl of the early thirties is fairly well tied down by this time. Soil conservation there consists first of all in getting a good protecting cover on the land again. Some of the land can be used for cultivated crops if they are planted when there is enough moisture in the soil. Other parts of the Dust Bowl must always remain in grass. Land that is best used for growing grass is good land for raising livestock—as long as it is given decent treatment.

Dust storms result from blowing topsoil

Ancient troubles

This city was lost for 1,200 years. It was built in North Africa about A.D. 100, by a Roman emperor, and at one time we believe more than 25,000 people lived in it. In many ways this Roman city, Timgad, was like a modern American city. It had a public library, a great Roman forum, a theater that would seat 2,500 people, many fine public buildings, and public baths with beautiful mosaic floors. Great grain fields and orchards that provided the people with food surrounded it.

Timgad seemed destined for great things, but warlike nomad tribes poured out of the desert to conquer it, and by the seventh century after Christ the people of Timgad had either been killed or driven out.

Then the city disappeared. Winds began to blow the unprotected soil off the neglected land around the city. Dust piled in on Timgad and almost buried it. Sticking out of the sand was the proud Arch of Trajan—on the left in the picture—and the tops of a few columns. The land that once supported Timgad was ruined by wind and water erosion. Great gullies are found in it even yet.

About sixty years ago the French government began digging the city out of the drifted dust. The picture was taken after the digging was finished.

The nomads destroyed Timgad, and erosion ruined the land that once provided food for 25,000 people. But men were responsible. There are hundreds of millions of acres in the world that are in very much the same condition.

Wind erosion buried this ancient city for 1,200 years

Ancient remedies

Erosion is not a new thing. There are parts of the ancient world—in Syria, in the Holy Land, Persia, North Africa, Peru, and many other places—where the soil on which empires depended is now entirely gone. The land is so seriously damaged that the cost of putting it back into use would be staggering.

Ancient peoples tried in many ways to save their land. The picture shows what was done on a mountainside near Tripoli in North Africa, not far from Timgad. The work was done about three thousand years ago, on land we believe was once covered with a great forest of cedars of Lebanon.

The people made steps out of the steep slopes of the mountain. They built stone walls to hold back the soil that would otherwise have been washed away by rains. As the soil piled up behind the walls, it formed hundreds of little fields. But each one was level, and as a result the water did not run off, carrying precious soil with it, but sank slowly into the ground.

The hillside steps, properly known as bench terraces, cost a great deal to build. Engineers think they would cost us nowadays as much as five to ten thousand dollars an acre, or more. These North African terraces, and many others like them, have been in use for several thousand years.

In some parts of the world—for example in the Near East—people have tried to restore wasted land by bringing in good soil from somewhere else to cover the bare rocks. This would have been unnecessary if people had used the land properly in the first place.

Ancient people tried to stop erosion by building terraces

Erosion in colonial America

The early farmers in America had a great deal of trouble with soil washing. They did not know how to manage these new lands, under conditions so different from those in Europe. Many simply moved onto new land when they considered the old land "worn out."

George Washington was much concerned about erosion on his 8,000-acre Mt. Vernon estate. "No estate in United America is more pleasantly situated than this—on one of the finest rivers [the Potomac] in the world. Our lands were originally very good, but use and abuse have made them quite otherwise."

Our first President, who was also one of the best farmers of his day, recorded his thoughts in journals and letters. He wrote about gullies in his fields, which "previous to being sown with grain and grass-seeds, ought invariably to be filled up." "Brush and rubbish of all sorts," he told his manager, "are to be thrown into the gullies and covered over, so as to admit the ploughs to pass." The workmen were to get "rich mud" from the creek and spread it over the "poor and washed parts" of the fields. "By so doing, and a small sprinkling of manure thereon, they will acquire a green sward. . . . These are the only means I know of, by which exhausted lands can be recovered, and an estate rescued from destruction."

Washington was writing shortly after the Revolution. James Madison and Thomas Jefferson are famous for other reasons, but they too wrote about the land troubles. Men like these foresaw problems and did a great deal to educate farmers and the public in their day.

George Washington had a good deal of trouble with erosion at Mt. Vernon

Erosion and people

If erosion is allowed to continue, the people who work on the land—the farmers—can get into serious trouble. Where gullies get a good start, cultivation may have to stop. As the topsoil gets thinner, the soil that is left does not produce as well as it once did. Eroded land not only produces less, but what it does produce is usually not as good.

It still costs the farmer as much as ever to grow crops, but he does not get as much for his work as he did before erosion started. Farmers have to borrow money to make ends meet. If the land gets poor enough, they may finally have to quit. Many thousands of farmers have given up and gone to work at something else for just such reasons.

All told, there are some 740 million acres of land in our country that have been injured, or that can be injured very easily, by erosion. This figure excludes Federal lands, and lands used for cities, roads, and airports. Unless this land is wisely used, we could have more and very serious land problems.

Whether we are farmers or not, we have an interest in the land and who is using it. If it is used wisely—and that is what conservation means—we and our children can have enough food to eat and of the right kind. If the land is wasted by erosion, one of these days future Americans may have to go on shorter rations. Widespread damage to land means less food for us all, to say nothing of poorer food, dust storms, ruined farmers, wasted land, muddy rivers, mud–filled reservoirs, and floods with all their disaster.

Erosion can result in ruined land and wasted lives

THE BASIS
FOR SOIL CONSERVATION

Erosion studies

A number of years ago American scientists began studying the way erosion takes place and methods of stopping it or preventing it from starting.

The picture shows one of the research stations where this important work is going on. The big tanks catch and measure the water and soil that wash off the small plots of land above them when it rains. By treating the plots in various ways, it is possible to find out how erosion takes place under all sorts of conditions. Different kinds of plants can be grown on the plots or new methods of stopping erosion can be tried on them.

From studies like these we have found out, for example, that an acre of land can lose as much as an inch of topsoil in a single year. On soil like this, seven inches of topsoil can be washed off in seven years, if the soil is left entirely bare. If corn were planted on the same soil, it would take eleven years to lose the seven inches. If the soil were planted with thick-growing grass, it would take thirty-four thousand years to lose the same amount of soil. Other types of soil show different results. But it is clear that the kinds of plants growing on the soil, and forming a cover on it, have a great deal to do with how fast it erodes.

One of the important facts we have found out is that *if soil has a cover on it, water does not wash it away.*

Tests must go on for a long time before we know everything we need to know about soil conservation, though possibly we know more than any other country in the world.

At research stations scientists study ways to prevent erosion

No more burning

Fire is one of the greatest enemies of the soil. It destroys the cover of vegetation that protects the soil, and it burns up plant and animal remains that would otherwise have enriched and become part of the soil itself. Burning seems to be an easy way to get rid of brush or weeds or other plants that are in the way. But it is a careless and costly tool to use because it usually does so much more damage than good.

People burn the land for many reasons. Some farmers burn brushy fence rows and other areas to kill insect pests. But they usually do it in the wintertime, when the plants are dry and dormant but when most insects are living in the ground.

Fire in the forest may destroy a crop of timber it has taken nature many years to grow. The young trees—the new forest—are nearly always consumed, and the soil-burning mulch of dead and decaying leaves on the forest floor is ruined. Worst of all, the forest soil is laid open to the action of wind and water, which may carry away the topsoil.

In the picture, stacks of pea plants in an open field are being burned after the peas have been harvested. If the plants were spread out on the field, they would help protect the soil from washing away. They would also decay, after they were plowed under, and add to the fertility of the soil.

Often we have to unlearn something we thought we knew. The practice of burning is one of these, though it is not employed much on farms and ranches now because soil conservationists have shown the owners why it does not pay.

Burning is wasteful, out of date, destructive

Soil surveys

In order to practice soil conservation, we need to know as much as possible about soils. We must have facts about where the good soils and the poor ones are, about the depth of soil, whether it erodes easily or not, how productive it is, how far to bedrock, and a great many other things.

There are about seventy-five thousand kinds of soil in our country, and getting enough information about each of them is a big job. This work, started in 1899, is known as the National Cooperative Soil Survey. The Federal and State governments are cooperating in the huge job of mapping the soils on nearly two billion acres. Already a third of the total land area of America has been mapped, including about half of all the land in farms.

The men who make the survey are called soil scientists. They put all the facts about the soils on an aerial photograph of the land. Soil layers beneath the surface of the ground must be examined, and sometimes a complete core of soil, with all parts in place, is collected. These soil cores are studied in laboratories to find out how fast water can move through them, how dense they are, and so on. Other samples are checked for their water-holding capacity, or for the presence of certain minerals. Large samples may be tested to see how well the soil can be compacted—for highway or dam construction.

After a field map is finished, it is prepared for publication. The reports are of key importance to land owners, soil conservationists, and many others. They provide a scientific base for dealing with land and water problems.

Soil scientists map the soils

Field surveys are backed up by laboratory work

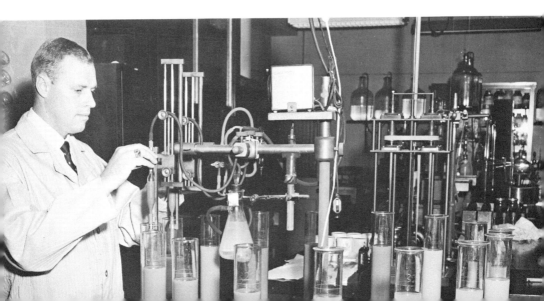

Classifying land and soils

Our scientists have found that some soils behave just about the same as a number of others, so they can be grouped as though they were a single kind. Some groupings work well for farming, others work well for planning roads, or for urban or suburban planning, or for recreation or wildlife purposes.

One such grouping, of very wide use, is what is called a land capability classification. There are eight classes in this grouping which express the amount of risk for agriculture and the limits within which each kind of soil can be used. Sub-classes tell the kind of risk, and then capability units group the soils that take the same kind of treatment.

For example, Class I land is level, fertile land that will go on producing good crops as long as it is fertilized and well managed. Class II land may be just as good, but with gentle slopes where erosion is something of a problem. We could call this Class IIe—the *e* standing for erosion. Any soils that take the same treatment might be given the capability unit designation IIe 1 or 2 or 3, depending on the treatment. Steeper land, or land with more difficult problems, would fall into higher classes. Classes VI to VIII include lands that ordinarily cannot be cultivated.

In the picture, there are several classes of land, all in danger of erosion. The steepest slopes should go into carefully protected woodland, hay, and pasture grasses. Lesser slopes are cultivated and protected by strip cropping, contour cultivation, and terraces. The best land in the valley bottom is well fertilized, and good crop rotations are used on it.

Lands on the hills in the background are Class VI; in the valley, Class I; on the hill in the foreground, Class III

Testing new plants

This picture shows one of the many American nurseries, called Plant Materials Centers, where new plants of possible use in soil conservation work are being tested. Grasses, legumes, shrubs, trees from anywhere in the world are tried out here.

The plants that are tested must first of all withstand the climate. They are planted out in short rows or blocks and kept under close observation for a number of years. In the meantime the scientists try various methods for seeding and growing them. They are tested in mixture with other plants, on various kinds of soil and in different situations and conditions.

The most promising plants are then taken out and tried in field plantings with the help of interested farmers or ranchers. They are observed and checked very closely from time to time. When the observers are satisfied that they have a plant that can do the job they want, they begin to increase it. The parent material, or foundation stock as it is called, is grown in the Center. Farmers and ranchers willing to raise the plant under rigidly controlled conditions are engaged to increase it. Finally, the plant is put in the hands of commercial seedsmen or nurserymen for general sale.

Hundreds of plants are tested, but only a very few survive the rigorous tests. Some plants may turn out to be useful only at high altitudes. Some may grow best only in combination with other plants. Some may grow well in one part of the country, but nowhere else. We need to remember that we have a great variety of conditions in the United States.

A station in Kansas where promising conservation plants are tested

LAND FOR CULTIVATION

Contour cultivation

In the past American farmers took pride in plowing their land in straight lines. The man who could plow the straightest furrow was supposed to be the best farmer. For many years we held contests and gave prizes to these "best farmers."

But when furrows run downhill, they help water take the shortest possible course to the lowland. Naturally the steeper the hill, the faster the water pours down the furrows, carrying more and more soil with it. Straight furrows, therefore, running downhill, help to make erosion worse.

The best way to plow furrows so that water cannot run down them is to plow them *across* the slope. If they are exactly level, they interfere with water that is trying to run down the hill. When farmers plow this way they cannot plow a straight furrow. Instead, their furrows wind in and out, running around the hills, always on the level.

Level cultivation is known more correctly as contour cultivation because it fits the contours of the land. Farmers who practice contour cultivation have found that it is easier to walk on the level than it is to walk uphill and downhill, and that it does not take as much gasoline for your tractor nor as many horses to do the work.

The old idea of the straight furrow is giving way to the new idea of the level furrow. This is not only scientifically correct, it is common sense. The level furrows keep the rain from running away and keep the topsoil in place.

Contour cultivation is a simple practice, but it is basic to soil and water conservation work.

Contour cultivation blocks the flow of water downhill, prevents erosion

Strip cropping

Even though level furrows will stop and hold a great deal of water, they may not be enough to hold the water resulting from heavy rains. They need help on soils that wash easily or on slopes that are very steep.

Some crops, such as corn, protect the soil very little, even though they are planted and cultivated on the contour. Other crops, such as grass or clover, do a much better job because the plants grow very close together. By putting strips or bands of these close-growing crops between strips of corn, erosion can be slowed down considerably. Water may start to spill over the level furrows in the strip of corn and run downhill. But when it runs into the grass strip it slows down, drops the soil it is carrying, and soaks into the ground.

Farming in level strips like this is called strip cropping. It will not stop all erosion, but it helps a lot. Usually the strips must be combined with other conservation practices. In hilly country they are almost always used with contour cultivation, and very often with the terraces shown on page 71.

Each year the strips are changed. In one strip, corn may be planted one year and a close-growing crop the next. By changing the crops in the strips, the soil is improved, as we shall see on page 82. Strip cropping, especially when it is used along with other conservation practices, not only saves soil but increases yields of crops.

At first the patterns that result from using strips on the contour were considered startling, but they are really very beautiful and fit the land better than the old square fields.

Strip cropping helps prevent erosion

Terraces

On a great deal of land in the United States, contour cultivation and strip cropping are not enough to check the flow of water and prevent soil from washing away. On such land terraces must be used to control it. The terraces we build are different from the terraces used by people of ancient times (page 46). Theirs were like big steps on the hillside. The modern soil conservation terraces are low, rounded ridges of earth built across the sloping hillsides to stop water flowing straight downhill. They are built around the curves of the hills.

Where the land is almost flat and there is very little rain, terraces are built exactly level—on the contour. Terraces on the Great Plains, such as the one in the picture, are usually level. They are built to catch and hold all the water that falls and hold it until it soaks into the soil. Thus they help store water in the ground for the growing crops.

Where slopes are steep and there is a great deal of rain, terraces cannot be built exactly on the level. If they were, they would fill up with water and break over. In country like this, therefore, the terraces slant very slightly downward. Water that collects on the uphill side of the terrace flows gently along the terrace until it reaches some place where it can be safely taken off the field. This is to prevent the water from flowing so swiftly that it cuts into the soil.

If terraces had steep slopes on both sides, farm machinery would tip over if the farmer tried to run over them. Modern terraces are built with gentle slopes on both sides so that they can be planted and cultivated like the rest of the field.

Terraces being constructed

Finished terracing system in use

Waterways

A level terrace has no outlet. It is blocked at both ends so that the water it backs up can soak into the soil. When terraces have a gentle downward slope, a good deal of water may collect behind them, and it must be carried off slowly and carefully so that it does not start cutting into the soil. It would be unwise to let this water spill out into woodland or a bare roadside ditch because it might start cutting a gully.

In order to help water from terraces flow safely off the fields, terrace outlet channels, or waterways, are used. These waterways are broad, gently sloping channels covered with a good thick carpet of grass. In the picture, a grassed waterway of this sort winds through a strip-cropped field. The field is terraced, although the terraces cannot be seen because of the crop plants. Every time there is a heavy rain, water flows from the terraces onto the waterway and on down to a pond or stream below.

The waterway takes up a great deal of room in the field, but the land it is on is by no means wasted. The grasses growing on it are not only planted there to hold the soil, but they can also be used for pasture or a meadow. The farmer can easily drive a mowing machine over the waterway and cut the grass for hay. The waterway is broad because a broad channel will not erode as easily as a narrow one and, of course, it can carry more water.

When terraces are going to be built, the waterway must usually be installed first, otherwise water from the new terraces might pour onto the unprotected land.

Well-grassed waterways conduct water safely downhill

Hedges

On some kinds of land, hedges are used to help control erosion. They are planted in winding rows that follow the contours of the land, and are made of shrubs that grow six to eight feet high and do not spread out into the fields. The shrubs are planted close together so that they will form the best possible check to water trying to run downhill.

In some parts of the country, hedges are used as living fences. The hedge plants must be thick-growing and thorny so that cattle or horses cannot push through them. Sometimes the hedges are used to keep livestock out of gullies so that vegetation may grow up in the gullies and heal them. In the flat lands of the Great Plains, straight rows of shrubs are sometimes used to break the force of the wind and prevent the soil of crop fields from blowing away.

Hedges do much more than check the flow of water or the force of wind. They hold snow in drifts, so that as it melts in the spring, the water soaks into the ground for crop plants to use. They cut down the drying action of the wind. Hedges serve as permanent guide lines to follow in cultivation and planting on the level. They provide a place for insect-eating birds to nest and live, and in turn these useful birds feed on insect pests and help to protect the farmers' crops.

Many kinds of shrubs are used for hedges. Some of them bear fruits that farmers use for making jelly, pie, or preserves. Some have flowers that furnish nectar for honeybees, and nearly all offer shelter and food for quail, rabbits, raccoons, and other game and fur-bearing animals.

Hedges on the contour hold soil and are good places for wildlife too

Wind stripping

On the level stretches of the western plains where rainfall is scanty and winds blow with great force, strip cropping looks somewhat different than it does eastward. The strips run straight across the great flat fields, east and west, north and south—any direction that puts them directly across the path of the wind.

These western wind strips are used not to hold back water but to prevent soil blowing by the wind. Strips of wheat may be planted between strips of sorghum, a plant that looks something like corn. The sorghum strips grow taller than the wheat and break the wind; they also tend to lift the wind off the strips of wheat. If the fields were not stripped but were all in wheat, the wind could sweep across without hindrance. The wind has been known not only to cover the wheat plants in places by drifting soil, but also to blow patches of soil away from around the plants.

The sorghum is used for feeding cattle, so that the crops in both kinds of strips are useful. When the sorghum is cut and also when the wheat is harvested, the stalks of both of them may be left standing, as in the picture on page 89. Keeping the cut stalks on the surface of the ground helps to prevent wind erosion and to keep snow from drifting too much in winter.

There are vast areas in the northern part of the Plains especially, where nearly all cultivated land is wind-stripped in this way. The wind strips are back-stopped by other conservation measures, such as windbreaks and stubble mulching.

Strips against the wind in Montana; shelterbelts around the home

Windbreaks

On the open prairies and plains, the winds get a good clear sweep across the land. They can dry out the soil very quickly, and if there is no cover on it the topsoil begins to blow. The winds do other things as well, such as piling up the snow in great drifts during the winter, or blowing over corn and other crops.

One way to help cut down the bad effects of winds is to plant windbreaks across their path. Sometimes only a single row of shrubs is used, but often several rows of trees are planted with shrubs on the two outer sides. The trees and shrubs must be planted close together so that there is no place for the wind to drive through. Windbreaks in certain parts of the country, if they are well placed and of the right height, offer snug protection to the crops as well as the land.

Windbreaks have to be used with great care, so that they do not cause snow to drift into the wrong places, or take up too much land that ought to be in crops. Since the grasslands do not get much rain, not many trees and shrubs are able to live there. But for each part of the treeless country, we know a good deal about the best plants to use and how to place the windbreaks so that they will do the most good.

Windbreaks are often planted where they shelter the house, barn, and other farm buildings, and give cattle protection from winter winds. The shrubs furnish fruits for home use, and the trees provide occasional posts or fuel wood. The windbreaks make good cover, too, for pheasants, rabbits and other Plains wildlife.

Windbreaks block soil blowing

Legumes and soil conservation

For more than twelve centuries farmers in many parts of the world thought that some plants would actually improve the soil if they were grown on it. This may not seem very remarkable. Yet everyone knew that to grow grain, for instance, sooner or later you had to add fertilizer. If you didn't, the crops would get poorer and the soil become exhausted. But there were some plants that were different, and instead of using up the plant food in the soil, as most plants do, they added to it.

The plants that could do this included a number of beans and peas, clovers, vetch, alfalfa, and many others. All these belong in the same family—the Legume Family; that is, they are closely related plants. All the members of this family bear their seeds in pods known as legumes.

About 1888 scientists found out how legumes improved the soil. All legumes have little nodules on their roots, which contain bacteria that can extract nitrogen from the air. Nitrogen is an important plant food, but most plants have to get it from nitrogen compounds in the soil. If a soil is poor in these nitrogen materials, plants do not do well. But the bacteria of the legumes' root-nodules get nitrogen from the air in the soil. As they do this, they build up the nitrogen into compounds the legumes can use. When the legumes die, they leave the nitrogen in usable form for other plants.

Legumes can grow on soils that are very low in nitrogen, and so we use many legumes on eroded or impoverished soil to improve it. Sometimes the legumes are planted alone, but often they are mixed with grasses.

White clover, a legume widely used for pasturage

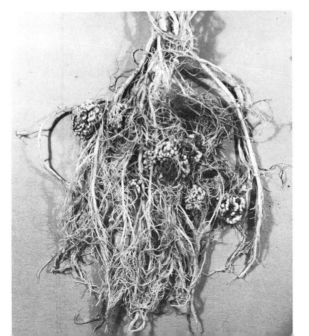

Nodules on legume roots contain nitrogen-fixing bacteria

Crop rotations

If you watch a field year after year you may see corn in it one year, wheat the next, and clover the next. Then the order of the crops may be repeated. This way of growing crops is called crop rotation.

By using a three-year rotation, the field is disturbed by cultivation only one year out of three—when it is in corn. The wheat plants have many fibrous roots that help to hold the soil in place, and the clover, being a legume, adds nitrogen. Sometimes clover is plowed under as a green manure crop, explained on page 84. Experiments have shown us that there is much less erosion under rotated crops than there is under a crop like corn grown year after year on the same land.

Strip cropping helps the farmer to grow crops in rotation, because he plants the strips to different crops each year. The upper picture shows corn in the strip near the top of the hill, wheat below the corn, and alfalfa below the wheat. The lower picture, taken the following year, shows wheat where the corn was, and then alfalfa and corn. The next year the order down the slope would be alfalfa, corn, and wheat.

Of course, many different crops are grown in rotation, depending upon the soil and part of the country. In the South, for example, oats or wheat are sometimes grown after cotton, and the third year a legume such as lespedeza is planted. Sometimes it takes five years or more to complete a rotation, and on steep slopes the land may be kept several years in hay or some other soil-protecting cover before a cultivated crop is grown again.

Changing crops on the land is good soil conservation

Green manure

We have already talked about the very great value of humus on page 28. There are many ways of getting it into the soil. The city gardener may add the leaves from the shade tree in the front yard or the clippings from his lawn. The farmer applies manure from the stables of his horses and cattle. He also plows under the residue of corn or wheat or other crops grown on the land. Sometimes straw, sod, grass clippings, manure, leaves and all are mixed with soil and piled up to rot. The resulting earthy material, known as compost and abundantly rich in humus, is then spread out upon the soil.

In the picture a farmer is adding humus in another way—by plowing under a crop planted especially for that purpose. Such a crop is called green manure. Often a grass, such as rye, is used. Most of the best green manure plants, however, are legumes such as clover or vetch or peas of different kinds. Legumes are chosen for the purpose not only because they provide humus when they decay, but because they also add nitrogen to the soil, as described on page 80.

The crop in the picture is sweet clover, a legume that is grown for green manure in many parts of our country. Sometimes a green manure crop is not plowed clear under, but is crushed down with a kind of plow called a disk and is left mixed with the very surface layer of soil. Occasionally it may simply be cut down and left lying on the ground to decay.

But whether humus comes from green manure, compost, animal manures, crop residues or from other sources, it enriches the soil and helps greatly to control erosion.

Plowing under a legume, sweet clover, for green manure

Winter cover for soil

If soil has a cover on it, water does not wash it away, but cultivated fields, of course, have a cover on them only while the crop is growing. In the South heavy rains may beat upon the unprotected soil all winter long and wash it away. In the North, even though the ground is frozen or covered with snow in the winter, the autumn rains and melting snow of spring carry away tons of fertile topsoil if the crop fields are not protected. So farmers plant a winter cover crop on them—a crop that will grow in cool weather and remain alive on the ground during the colder months.

The picture shows a heavy winter cover of crimson clover and vetch in an apple orchard. The rain and running water do not wash the soil while this thick growth remains upon it. When such a cover crop is full grown, the farmer may plow it under to add humus to the soil, but he does this at a season when there is not much erosion. In some orchards, the farmer may never turn the cover crop under but will keep it there all the year round. Grasses make a fine permanent cover.

Many different plants are used as winter cover crops in various parts of the country. In the northeastern states, vetch, rye, and winter grains are planted for this purpose. Sometimes a mixture of grass and clover is sown, or alfalfa and sweet clover. In the South, farmers use crimson clover, winter peas, and bur-clover, or mixtures of clover and grass, vetch and grain, or crimson clover and rye. In the Pacific Coast region, vetches, clovers of many kinds, mustard, and other plants provide the best winter cover.

Cover crops protect the soil

Use of crop residues

In the section on humus (page 28), we talked about how valuable humus can be in the soil. Soil conservationists recommend a special practice that makes use of humus. This involves using any plant residues that remain after a crop is harvested. The picture shows a corn field after the corn has been harvested. The cut stalks of the corn plants—known as stubble—are still in place on the left half of the field. On the right, the land has been plowed with the disk plow, which leaves a good bit of stubble on top of the ground. Disking does not turn the soil all the way over, but tips it only part way. This leaves a mulch of stubble to protect the soil.

Leaving a stubble mulch like the one in the picture is a first-class way to control erosion. The rough cover of corn stalks helps a great deal to prevent the wind from drying out and blowing the surface soil. The stalks gradually decay and add humus to the soil, and soil with humus in it does not wash or blow as easily as soil without humus.

Years ago people used to burn the stubble on grain fields, but today farmers using soil conservation methods make full use of any plant leftovers they have—whether grain stubble, pea vines, bean plants, or any other such material.

Mulching the soil with stubble also helps control grasshoppers in the Plains country. Grasshoppers lay their eggs in open, packed soil, but where the soil is rough and mixed with grain stubble, they do not lay as many eggs. In country where hordes of these insects devour whole fields of wheat or corn, this is very important.

Corn residues are disked into the soil for humus

Wheat stalks are used for humus and for protection against soil blowing

Field borders

Crop plants do not grow very well along the edge of a cultivated field that lies next to the woods. This strip of land is shaded by the woodland trees, and the tree roots reach out into the field to take most of the moisture and plant food. Every year the farmer plows close to the trees so that young trees and weeds will not get started in the strip. Because it is plowed every year, and because the crop grows there so poorly, the ground usually stays bare all through the season. Rain water collects from the crop rows and runs down the edge of the field, and as a result the field border is usually eroded. Sometimes a gully starts in just such a way.

In the picture you can see that the field border is well protected by a good plant cover. The plant in the border is used a great deal in the southern states. It is a legume, known as bicolor lespedeza, that enriches the soil by adding nitrogen to it. In midsummer it has beautiful lavender flowers that honeybees visit for nectar, for it makes an excellent honey. Its seeds attract quail which like to live in good field borders.

Farther north, where lespedezas do not grow, the border may be planted to berry-bearing shrubs. Sometimes the trees are cut back a little to let the wild shrubs underneath them get a chance to grow and thrive.

Field borders improved in such ways are especially valuable for encouraging many kinds of wildlife, particularly birds. These wild creatures help keep down insect pests and some, such as quail, are game birds as well.

Borders protect field edges, provide food and cover for wildlife

Irrigation

Growing crop plants in the drier parts of the West is an uncertain business unless there is extra water to make up for the lack of rain. On some thirty-eight million acres in these dry areas farmers add water by irrigation to be sure of a harvest.

Water usually flows through canals and ditches to reach the plants. Ideally the fields should be nearly flat, with only a slight tilt to them, so that the water can run evenly over the land. But usually the land has to be leveled by machinery.

Using irrigation water on large fields takes great skill, and soil conservation practices have to be used. If the water runs down the ditches too fast, it begins to carry soil away and may cause serious damage. So the land has to be leveled carefully, and the ditches, and outlets from them, built exactly right. If too much water is used, some parts of the field get too wet and have to be drained. That is why water must be measured. If too much water is applied, chemicals begin to come to the surface and make "alkali spots." When fields are saturated with chemicals, they can no longer be used to grow crops, and reclaiming them is very costly. Sometimes they cannot be reclaimed at all, and when this happens on a big scale, large areas of formerly valuable land may be abandoned.

In addition to surface irrigation, more than four million acres are irrigated by sprinklers in the West, and here, too, the sprinkler system must deliver measured amounts of water. In the East about six million acres are irrigated.

*Whether sprinkled on the land or conducted by ditches,
irrigation water must be carefully handled*

Drainage

Wet and soggy soil cannot be plowed and cultivated, and ordinary crops will not grow in it. Yet a great deal of rich agricultural land in the United States was once too wet to farm and only became useful after the water was drained off. In Ohio, Indiana, Illinois, and Iowa, in Michigan and Minnesota, in Arkansas and Louisiana and elsewhere, drained swamps and marshes now form some of our most fertile farms. There are still nearly forty-five million acres of our land that need drainage to make them produce as much as they can.

Land is drained in several ways. Very often the farmer lays short sections of small tile pipe in shallow ditches dug across a field. The ditches are filled in and the water from the field collects in the pipes by seeping between the sections, which are not cemented together. The water then runs through the tiles into an open ditch which carries it off into a creek or low place where it does not interfere with farming. Sometimes, instead of laying tile, the farmer digs an open ditch like the one in the picture. Water drains directly from the soil into the ditch and then runs off the field.

Sometimes the only way a farmer can reduce erosion on steep hillsides is to change them from crop fields to pasture or woodland. But he can only do this if he can find another place to grow his cultivated crops. Such a place may be found in wet bottomland if it is drained.

Not all wet land should be drained, for some of it is not good soil anyway and is most useful as it is. Swamps often produce valuable trees, and marshes can support wildlife.

*Tile drains, later covered over (above)
and opening up a main drain ditch (below)*

LAND NOT CULTIVATED

Orchards

Possibly the land on which we grow our fruit trees and grapevines will be the last to show the new soil conservation patterns. Trees grow slowly, compared to the annual crops such as wheat or corn, and orchards are not easily changed from one year to the next. Erosion is no less common in orchards, however, than on other crop lands. Almost everywhere that apples, pears, peaches, grapes, and citrus fruits are grown, washed and gullied slopes may be found beneath the orchard trees and vines. But gradually even our orchards and vineyards, as well, are coming to be arranged according to the contours of the land.

High above a citrus grove in California, an airplane photographer snapped this picture that at first glance may puzzle you. What you see are rows of trees, orange trees, that curve in and out on the hillsides, the rows always on the level.

The orchard rows are level because contour cultivation pays in a citrus grove or an apple orchard, just as it does with other kinds of crops. Rain water, or water brought to the orchard by irrigation ditches, is held on the hillsides that are terraced and cultivated on the contour. The trees in this orchard are planted on terraces, much like those built by the people of ancient times, shown on page 47.

Orchards must also have cover crops planted among the trees to protect the soil and perhaps to provide green manure as well. Better yet, a permanent cover of grass sown on the floor of the orchard provides year-round protection for the soil and a cleaner place for fruit to fall.

Meadows

Land that has a good crop of hay on it is well protected against erosion. The hay plants grow thickly as long as they are in good condition, and dashing rain or strong winds cannot get at the soil beneath them. Even when the hay is cut, the stubble remains behind to form a cover.

Hay is usually planted on land that is steeply sloping or that will wash away very easily if it is cultivated. Frequently this thick-growing crop is used in every other strip of a strip-cropped field. And where waterways are used to carry water from terraced fields, hay again can do the job.

We use both grasses and legumes for hay. The grasses grow on poorer, drier soils than the legumes do, but some of the legumes make better hay for feeding livestock. Timothy and orchard grass, sudan grass, crested wheatgrass, and reed canary grass are the common grasses used for hay. Alfalfa heads the list of legumes as the best of all hay crops, but red clover, sweet clover, and lespedeza are also valuable and widely used.

Wherever hay is planted, it has to be kept in good, healthy condition if it is to yield abundantly and protect the soil. Fertilizers have to be used on it liberally, and the hay must not be cut too often nor too short. Weeds that get in can be cut off by a mowing machine when they grow above the hay plants. Meadows do not yield a high value crop, but hay is vital for our livestock and an excellent cover for certain kinds of land.

Meadow land in thick-growing hay is safe from erosion

Odd areas

On almost every farm or ranch there are areas that are too rough or too poor to use for cultivated crops. They are usually too small and scattered to make good pastures or woodlots but they need not be idle or wasted. Very often they need only protection from fire and grazing to make them productive of valuable wild fruits. Blackberries, elderberries, hazelnuts, wild plums, and many other native fruits, can grow on these areas.

Odd areas yield other things as well. On rough slopes, such as the one shown in the picture, pheasants and quail may make their nests and find shelter and retreat, and they are good places for fur animals like the skunk, whose pelt brings cash to the trapper. The odd place is proof that no parcel of land is without value, and that there is no reason for idle land. We have to learn to recognize the value of land and learn too how to use it wisely.

Often small in themselves, odd areas, marshes and similar places add up to a total of more than ninety million acres. Sometimes the farmer tries to pasture these areas, but when they are rocky or infertile they are very poor places for good grass. If he tries to cultivate them he wastes labor, seed, fertilizer, and equipment, trying to grow a crop where the land is unfit for crops and where he may reap only erosion. But if these odd areas are set aside and protected for wild plants and animals, and appropriate cover is kept on the land, they are protected from erosion and yield many products of value.

Little spots are useful when protected

Land in pasture

A good pasture is a fine protector of the soil. Under a thick, lush layer of grasses, clovers, and other pasture plants, the topsoil is almost perfectly preserved. But it takes skill and great care to develop and use a really fine pasture.

If too many cows or sheep are put on a pasture to graze, they will eat too much of the grass or clover. The plants cannot grow fast enough to keep up with the appetites of the animals and they begin to die. As the plants die, the animals chew at what is left, until pretty soon the pasture begins to wear out, much like a frayed carpet. A worn pasture is a poor cover for soil, and the worse it gets, the worse erosion becomes.

One of the secrets of good pasture management is knowing *when* to put livestock on it, *how many* animals to put on, and when to take the animals *off*. If the animals get on the ground too early in the spring, they may trample the pasture plants into the soft earth. If too many animals are on the pasture, or if they are left on too long, they are likely to eat themselves out of food. Only by balancing the number of animals and the amount of grass or clover that can be safely grazed can a pasture be kept in first-class shape.

Pasture plants have to be fertilized—just like corn or other crop plants—and weeds and brush must be kept down. Pastures look different in various parts of the country. In some places they are carpets of grass, in other places they may be several feet thick with sweet clover. But the plants have to be kept in good condition if both land and livestock are to benefit.

A well-managed pasture is good both for animals and soil

Range land

In the western half of the United States, about three quarters of the land is used for grazing livestock. Some of the range is level grassland but a great deal of it is rocky or mountainous and partly covered with trees or shrubs.

Most of the western range is dry country, and the grasses and other plants are not as thickly set or luxuriant as they are in wetter climates. An acre of really good pasture in the East, for example, can support a cow for the summer. But on good grass range in the West it takes two or three acres to support a single cow for a month, and on poor range it may take ten to twenty acres or more.

In the early days we seriously mistreated our western range by putting more cattle on it than the vegetation could support. The over-grazing and trampling caused the better grasses to die out, and their place was taken by inferior grasses, shrubs, and weeds. At the same time erosion became very serious, especially in the areas where the over-grazing was heaviest. Range experts estimate that possibly no more than 5 to 10 per cent of the range was in really good condition about 1930, but today the picture is very different. About a third of the range is in good to excellent condition, with about two thirds still fair to poor.

The picture shows a piece of excellent range land in Utah. The land in the foreground was formerly in sagebrush, but has been reseeded to good range grasses. There are few or no weeds and the range is now producing up to ten times as much forage as it did before.

Good range protects soil, produces more livestock

Improving range land

Raising livestock on the range calls for great skill. If the grass begins to get thin, the animals must be moved. In wintertime, livestock has to be fed on hay or some other feed because the range cannot be used the year round. No more animals must be put on the range than it can safely support.

When cattle or sheep are on the range, the animals must be well spread out, because wherever they collect in one place they eat all the grass. Sometimes they are driven slowly from one part of the range to another by cowpunchers or sheepherders. They can also be scattered by using well-placed water holes and blocks of salt. Where there is only one place for livestock to drink, the animals will not go far from it, and the grass nearest the water is grazed too closely. If drinking places are evenly spaced, the animals travel from one well or spring to another. Livestock must also have salt, and they will go a long way to get it. When big lumps of salt are laid out so that there is some on all parts of the range, then the animals do not stay in one place.

As ranchers ride the range, they can spot the plants that tell them what is happening. If the better grasses are increasing, the range is getting better, but if the poorer grasses and weeds are increasing, the range is getting poorer.

The range conservationist in the picture is an expert. He is checking the condition of the range, and he and the rancher will go over the information he collects and study it. Using the latest scientific methods, the rancher will go ahead to make the improvements his range may need.

A range rider checks condition of the range

Woodland

The top picture shows a healthy, vigorous woodland. The trees are of all sizes, and there is a fine understory of shrubs and young trees. Also there is a soft, thick mulch of dead leaves and twigs on the ground. A woodland such as this offers an almost perfect protection to the soil. Wild life of many kinds is at home here, and insect pests or diseases rarely become troublesome under these balanced, natural conditions. Every few years the man who owns this woodland can cut a few choice timber trees, that are later replaced by younger trees. Erosion never becomes destructive under such a luxuriant cover, and occasionally cutting down a large tree does no harm.

In woodland that is not well managed, in the lower picture, the undergrowth and young trees have been eaten and trampled by livestock. The woodland becomes thinner as the older trees die. The cattle trample the soft earth into mud, and gradually erosion gets a chance to operate. The cattle get little food, and what they get is of poor quality, grown in the shade. This is neither good pasture nor good woodland.

The two great enemies of woodland are fire and livestock. A really severe fire may burn off the trees, destroy the mulch, and even scorch the soil itself. Erosion may then damage the land still further.

Three simple things can keep a woodland healthy, vigorous, and productive. The first is to keep fire out. The second is to keep livestock out. The third is to cut trees a few at a time when they are big enough—rather than all at once.

Well-managed woodland protects soil, produces timber and other products

SPECIAL LANDS
AND SPECIAL TREATMENTS

Stream banks

Like cultivated fields, stream banks wash away when there is no cover on them. In the upper picture you see the edge of a stream which the water has cut into until the straight earth bank tumbles into the stream bed with every flood. The field above the bank is being slowly eaten away, to be carried downstream as sediment to clog the channel or fill a reservoir.

It is not easy and it costs a lot of money to stop stream bank erosion. But in the lower picture you can see the same place three years after the upper picture was taken. In the meantime the stream banks had been sloped and mats of willow boughs had been fastened securely to the banks. The willow boughs, with their stubs in the water, took root and began to grow. Soon they made a thick cover heavy enough to protect the banks from the cutting action of the rushing water.

In order to keep the new growth of willows on the stream bank, it is necessary to keep livestock away. Where streams flow through pastures, the cows will eat the young willow leaves and branches. They also trample the bank, helping to kill the willow roots, and they disturb the soil so that the bank erodes more easily.

It is also very important, if the bank is to remain protected by the willows, that the amount of water rushing down the stream in flood time be reduced. This can be done by protecting the watershed; that is, the hills and valleys where the rains fall that finally flow down the stream. By using the proper soil conservation measures, floods can be reduced and stream bank erosion really checked.

Stream banks erode unless protected

From gully to pond

In the top picture you can see an ugly scar on a once beautiful land-scape, where a long gully has cut through the fields. Not long ago this land was well on its way to ruin. But a dam was built across the lower part of the gully, and the lower picture shows a big pond that now covers the whole badly eroded area. Look closely and you will see it is the same place.

Ponds like this one are useful in many ways. They can provide a farm with bluegill sunfish and black bass—both excellent fish for any table. A pond can often produce more pounds of fish than a pasture can produce pounds of beef or mutton. If the water is fer-tilized—and farmers do this, just as they fertilize their fields or gar-dens—at least twice as many pounds of fish can be caught each year.

At the pond wild ducks may nest, or raccoons and muskrats find a home. If the pond is large enough, there is no better place to swim or boat, and under a nearby tree is a fine place to have a picnic. In the northern parts of our country, ponds provide farmers with ice. Wherever they are near the house or barn, they supply water for fighting fire. They also furnish water for spraying orchards, watering small gardens, and for livestock to drink. The well-managed pond always has a fence around it so that cattle cannot trample the shores or foul the water. Water for livestock is made available in a trough below the dam, outside the fence.

A pond like this one makes a fine place to have fun. Many farmers provide some camping areas around the edges of their ponds and rent them to campers who like to fish and swim.

Wasted land can make a good pond

Beaver dams

Beavers are soil conservationists of long experience. The dams they made in America before the white men came helped control run-off of water as well as erosion. They also helped to build meadows along mountain streams, since the water backed up by their dams collected banks of sediment.

Today beavers are not so abundant, but they are being captured alive to be released along streams where their little dams are needed to hold back the water. Care is taken not to put the beavers where they are likely to get at fruit trees. Neither are they desirable where the water held by their dams will flood crop fields or pastures or roads. But in the hills and mountains near the headwaters of streams they are very useful. Engineers estimate that a dam in one stream, built by a pair of beavers within two years after they were released, could not have been built by men today for less than ten thousand dollars.

A Wyoming rancher with a forty-acre hay meadow beside some beaver ponds, which covered about twenty acres of land along the stream, thought that if he could trap the beavers, destroy their dams, and let the water drain from the twenty acres, he would then have sixty acres of land to cut for hay. He trapped the beavers and drained the ponds. But, to his surprise, he then cut less hay from sixty acres than he had done from forty. The meadows without the ponds near by had become too dry to grow good hay. So the rancher put beavers back in the stream, the beavers rebuilt the dams, the water table rose, and the rancher once again cuts a good crop of hay each year.

Dams built by America's foremost conservationist, the beaver

From gully to woodland

Not all gullies will make good ponds. Instead they may be repaired in other ways. Many of them are planted to trees or other plants that protect them against erosion.

If a gully is to be planted, the first thing to do is to cut off the water that is washing the gully deeper. The fields above it must be protected by the many kinds of conservation practices we have already described. Cultivated land must be contoured, terraces or strip crops installed, good crop rotations begun. Hay must be planted on steeper slopes or good pasture made on them. These practices on the fields above will keep a great deal of water from running into the gully, but often it may be necessary to dig a ditch around the head of the gully, or build a terrace that will carry the water away from the place where it has been cutting the soil.

The gully must also be protected from livestock that would eat up the vegetation and trample the banks. It must often be fenced. Sometimes a hedge of thorny bushes is planted around the gully to keep out cattle, sheep, and horses. Protected from grazing animals and with the water kept out of it, a gully at last begins to heal.

The gully in the lower picture has been planted to trees and shrubs. This picture was taken just four years after the upper one, which shows how bad the gully was at one time. The trees will provide the farmer with wood products and the shrubs offer extra cover and food for wildlife.

Gully control is very expensive and it is much cheaper to prevent gullies than it is to reclaim them.

Wasted land can grow useful plants

Marshland

The marshes and swampy areas of America have not always been used wisely. Some wet areas, after the water was drained off, made good farmland, but many others turned out to be worthless. It is not always possible to tell whether the results of draining will be good or bad, but for marshes that we are sure cannot be made into farmland, there are many other good uses.

Coastal marshes are the natural home of wild duck, geese, and other water and shore birds. Some of these areas have been set aside as refuges for wildfowl, as well as for rare birds such as the wood ibis and the spoonbill. Inland marshes, too, are used in many states as refuges.

Marshy areas are productive of wild fur animals of great value. Farmers may gain sizeable incomes from muskrat, mink, and other fur-bearers. From all the marshes and swamps of our country in recent years we have trapped upward of five million muskrats annually. Their pelts were valued at nearly nine million dollars.

Some cities depend for their water supply on water that is stored or flowing underground. This supply sometimes depends on the water held in marshlands. The ill-advised draining and burning of the great Everglades marshes of Florida some years ago, for example, did a good deal of harm to the water supply of cities along the eastern coast.

The careful use of marshlands can help us preserve sources of wildfowl and fur animals, and may aid in preserving ground water supplies.

Muskrat home in a marsh

Land for highways

Anyone who drives an automobile knows that it can easily skid on a wet road. But a wet road sometimes has another, hidden, danger. When it rains on a road, the water has to run off somewhere, and it usually flows onto the sides of the road. Wherever the road goes up or down hill, the water may become a pretty good stream that cuts a gully alongside the highway. If the side of the road is bare and unprotected, the water can do a great deal of damage. It may cut under the road itself, cut out fences, or run off across farm fields, making a gully as it goes and carrying away tons of topsoil.

Bare cuts and roadbanks often produce enormous tonnages of sediment. This may wash onto the road itself, causing a safety hazard; removing it costs money. Or the sediment may go on downstream to fill up reservoirs or to be deposited along streambanks.

Keeping a road in good condition is very costly. Roads are now being built so that water running off them cannot destroy the roadsides or injure the road itself. The sides of the road may be given gentle slopes that are planted in grass and perhaps also in trees or shrubs. The water is carefully led by outlets to the nearest stream.

The photograph shows a road after treatment. The water can still flow down the hill, but on a good grass sod. When it reaches the bottom of the hill, it is carried away by culverts and taken to a stream. A roadside like this is easy to keep in good shape. The grass can easily be mowed by machinery, the view is more pleasant, and driving is made safer.

The right of way of a good highway is well protected

Land for wildlife

Almost all the land in our country was once free for wildlife, except for some cultivation by a small population of Indians. The settlement of America changed all that. Many kinds of wildlife were wiped out.

Wild creatures must have reasonable protection from hunting, and they need land and water to live on. The first wildlife refuge in the United States was set up only in 1903. This was five-acre Pelican Island off the coast of Florida, set up by a society of scientists and students of birds. Later the Federal government took this over, and set up many more wildlife refuges. Today many millions of acres are set aside as State or Federal wildlife refuges.

But many more millions of acres have been set aside by farmers and ranchers, and other private land owners and operators. These areas on private lands are hard to identify. Some of them are along streams on land that cannot be safely used for anything else, and some consist of reclaimed gullies. Others include the odd waste areas scattered in fertile fields, or are to be found in the borders of fields. Some surround ponds and lakes and some are on strip-mined areas, planted up to shrubs and trees.

We have learned that it is possible to have an abundance of songbirds, shore birds, water birds, small mammals and big ones, if places are provided for them to live. This is done partly by setting aside for the smaller birds and mammals smaller areas, which can also be used for other purposes.

Wildlife needs land—and water—too.

Land for suburbs

People who live in the suburbs rarely think of themselves as farmers. They are not, of course, but they are users and managers of the land they live on, and they may have any one of many land problems.

Anyone intending to buy a suburban home should first of all make a careful check of the property. He must be sure his house is not in a low place which can be flooded. Many home-owners have found out the hard way that little streams that look so harmless can be very terrible when they flood. Secondly, it is important to know whether the soil on any hillside property will hold up the house. Some soils will slip—and when they do, homes may be damaged beyond repair. Thirdly, if the suburban home is to use a septic tank for sewage disposal, it is well to be sure that the soil is permeable enough to take up the overflow.

Areas that are as built up as many suburbs are likely to be more than half covered with buildings and pavement. Water pours off roofs, driveways, parking areas, and streets. Storm sewers exist to dispose of all this excess water.

Suburbs that are new have a great deal of exposed soil, and until lawns are in place, and gutters and driveways installed, the uncontrolled water speeds off and down, carrying soil. Low areas may get wet and soggy, and mud may be deposited literally on the front doorsteps of the luckless suburbanite.

Suburban soil often needs the addition of wood chips, lawn clippings (spread thin), and other organic materials. Fertilizer will certainly be needed, and perhaps lime.

Paved areas have run-off problems

Unstable soil makes poor foundations

Land for outdoor recreation

Recreation includes a great variety of activities. For some people it is hunting deer or bears or elk, and for others it is watching or photographing birds, or identifying wild flowers. Other people like sports such as skiing, boating, or ice-skating, some enjoy camping or picnicking, and some enjoy simply driving through beautiful countryside. But whatever you like to do out of doors, it takes land and water to make it possible.

We have set aside land in our national parks and forests and refuges which is of special interest. The most scenic and spectacular areas are to be found in our national parks. Places like Yellowstone, Yosemite, White Sands, the Great Smokies, and many smaller areas of unique and special interest are included in these parks, both national and state. Millions of Americans visit these remarkable places every year. And millions visit our national and state forests and wildlife refuges.

A host of other recreational areas can be found in every state. These include ski areas, lakes, ponds, picnic grounds, dude ranches, camping areas, nature trails, scenic areas, bridle paths, and other areas of great variety.

Each year some 130 million Americans are out looking for places where they can enjoy themselves, and each year we spend about twenty billion dollars on outdoor recreation. We suspect we will be spending twice that amount—or maybe more—twenty years from now. All this takes land and water, and is going to take more.

Many kinds of land are required for recreation

Land for study

In the pictures you can see a group of young people learning about a pond and its values. In the lower one, Boy Scouts are learning about topsoil and its importance. You can learn a great deal by reading books, but the best way of all to learn about what goes on in the outdoors is to go out and see for yourself.

The lands and waters of America offer the most fascinating and wonderful places to visit. All the things described in this book—and a great many more—are yours to see and learn about. It doesn't take a large area either. It is wonderful to visit a great wildlife refuge to see grizzly bears, or elk and deer, or vast clouds of waterfowl. But it is also highly interesting to learn about the plants and animals and soil on just a little area.

In the United States many areas are being set aside for study of wildlife, soils, forest, range, marshes, swamps, ponds, and lakes. Sometimes these areas are called Nature Trails or Preserves. Sometimes they are bits of land alongside schools; they may be camp areas of the Boy Scouts or Girl Scouts, or other young people's groups. Often enough they have no name at all—they're just good places to learn about land and water and wild creatures.

Land can also be used for study

ACTION FOR CONSERVATION

Soil conservation districts

All that we know about soil conservation is worth very little unless it is put to use. We know how to prevent soil erosion, and how to use and improve all kinds of land so that they will be fully productive in their proper use. How do we go about getting something done about all this?

Ever since 1938, when the first soil conservation district was established, landowners in the United States have been giving the answer to this question. Today nearly all the land in our country is included within the boundaries of such a district. There are about three thousand districts now, and they almost cover America.

Soil conservation districts are voted into being by the people who live in the area. They then develop a program that sets out what the people intend to do about conserving lands and waters. On the basis of this program the district can get assistance from various government agencies.

Districts get help from many other Federal and State agencies. They also get help of various kinds from businesses, industries, bankers, churches, service clubs, and many other organizations. Even though most districts do not have the power to levy taxes, they are able to carry out their programs with great effect. The members of the governing bodies get no salary; they are men and women who serve their neighbors willingly, because they believe in the importance of keeping the land in good condition. The movement to improve American land is one of the most dramatic events in our country in recent years.

Supervisors of a district discuss land problems with a soil conservationist

Making conservation plans

In each of the three thousand soil conservation districts in the United States, there are trained experts in soil and water conservation work. They come from the U.S. Soil Conservation Service, and they can provide technical and scientific help for the people who use the land. They work very closely with the governing bodies of the district, helping to carry out the district program.

People using the land—farmers, ranchers, and many other kinds of land owners and operators—apply to the district for help with soil problems on their lands. If the district accepts their application, they become *cooperators*. A cooperator is one who agrees to use his land in accordance with a conservation plan worked out between him and a professional soil conservationist.

The cooperator and the soil conservationist walk over the cooperator's land. They have a soil and land capability map, and they discuss various ways in which each kind of land can be used. Many things are discussed—best ways to use land, best treatments to use, what can be expected from this or that use and management. Many of the various conservation practices talked about in this book will be discussed. Finally, all this is put together in a written plan. This contains a soil map, a land use map, and a listing and description of the management to be used. This is a conservation plan, and it will deal with the property *as a whole*. The land user will make the final decision, however, on what action to take.

A landowner and a soil conservationist discuss a conservation plan of action

Applying conservation plans

Once a cooperator has a conservation plan for his land, the next step is to get the plan applied. This usually takes several years or more, because clearly it cannot all be done at once. Cooperators make the necessary changes gradually, while they keep on working and managing their land.

Gradually, all the land that is to be cultivated gets cultivated on the contour. Terraces may be installed, after waterways are established. A strip-cropping system may be worked out, with the proper rotations. Land in cultivation that should be retired is planted to pasture or woodland.

A pond that should be installed is staked out, and a contractor goes to work to prepare the dam and spillway. Fences are changed to keep livestock where they should be. Waterways with hay in them are figured in the amount of livestock feed the farmer needs. Pastures are planted, or old ones are renewed. Trees are planted on extremely steep slopes.

In the West, lands are leveled and readied for efficient irrigation. In wet areas, drainage ditches are dug to take off excess water, field borders are developed for wildlife, odd areas are fenced off, and gullies are planted and fenced, or perhaps dams convert them to ponds.

In suburban areas, the plan may call for better placement of houses, schools, and roads, to take advantage of the soil capabilities. Nature trails may be set out in natural woodland areas. Industrial sites may be set aside for development.

Soil scientists, engineers, soil conservationists, biologists, foresters may all be needed to help the cooperator.

Soil conservationist and farmer check the hillside slope,
preparing to change land use

Watershed work

A watershed is any area of land from which all the run-off water drains into the same stream. It can be small, like the land on a farm that drains into a little creek, or large, when its central stream is a river.

Whatever we do in the upper part of a watershed makes a difference downstream. If the land is unprotected and eroding, a great deal of water will run off, carrying sediment. This makes the water in the stream muddy, and with enough rain the stream may flood. If all the land in a watershed is protected by conservation measures, streams gradually stay clear, and there is much less chance of flooding. Furthermore, the run-off is usually gradual rather than sudden.

Of course, we cannot hope to stop all floods, but we can reduce flooding by conservation treatment on the land. We can reduce it still more by the use of small storage reservoirs. In the bigger streams, we can cut it down further by using big dams. But we need to use all these ways—conservation land treatment, small dams, big dams— to do the best job.

For these reasons, in recent years we have been doing more and more of our conservation work on a watershed basis. There are nearly 13,000 small watersheds in our country. Of these 65 per cent are in need of treatment. The small watershed work includes both land treatment and the use of small dams or other water management structures. In the picture you can see one of these dams. Very often the lake or pond is used not only for flood prevention, but also for city water supplies, for recreation, or for wildlife.

Dam high upstream on the Potomac River helps prevent floods, provides water for a nearby town

AND FOR THE FUTURE...

People and their land needs

There are more than 200 million people in our country now. Every year we have about 3 million more. If the population grows as fast during the next thirty years as it is growing now, there will be nearly 350 million Americans. By the time this comes about, we will require more of everything. We will need twice as many houses, apartments, schools, and jobs. We will need double the food and water we use now.

Many of these needs require land. Our food comes from land, as we have seen. Houses, schools, apartments, cities, roads, airports must all have land too. Often these needs will conflict.

Our scientists think our land can grow enough food for double the number of people we have now, or even a little more. This estimate allows for enough more land for cities, roads, houses, and so on, and extends until about the year 2000. After that we are not sure.

In recent years we have had surpluses of wheat and some other crops which we have been storing. But these surpluses are being used up, as we double our need for food.

The land planning we do must be expert. Once a city or a highway or an airport is built, it is scarcely practical to try to change it back into raising food. The wisest possible use of our land will be essential. We will need to use land not suited for crop production for other things. We will need to avoid using good crop land for other purposes, if we can. And on the land we use for the production of food, we will need to use the best possible soil conservation practices.

Most of the 2,000-acre watershed above this dam
is protected as it should be

Land for cities

The pattern of where people live has changed enormously since America was first settled, and it is still changing very rapidly. At first most people lived on farms. In 1900 there were about 30 million Americans living in cities. By the end of this century the number may reach 250 million.

This means that the cities will be larger, that they will cover more land. In 1900 cities had about 5 million acres of land inside their boundaries. By the end of the century they are expected to cover an area of about 41 million acres.

As our cities grow in size and population, they cause other changes in land, often at a great distance. There must be super-highways to connect the cities, and these take land. Somewhere there has to be land set aside for recreation. It has been estimated that as much as 100 million acres may be needed for this purpose by the end of the century.

We expect that our cities will keep spreading. There may, for instance, one day be a single city stretching from Portland, Maine, to Washington, D.C. All the people in these cities of the future must live on products of the land, as well as on the land itself.

Even though the land used for cities and the needs of city dwellers is likely to take up more than double the area used for this purpose now, this is not alarming. Land planners can see how we can cultivate several 100 million acres of land that we do not now use in this way, and we can step up the production of crops on many kinds of land.

Cities require increasing amounts of land

Highways connecting cities require land too

Our scientists move ahead

Toward the end of 1965, the President of the United States said, "One American farmer now feeds and clothes himself and thirty-two others besides—an achievement unmatched anywhere on earth." He went on to talk about the "miracle of American agriculture," and it is indeed something all Americans can be proud of.

In 1965 we were producing 35 per cent more than we were in 1950. In other words, every year we do about 2 per cent better than the previous year. There are many reasons for this continual improvement in productivity. We use more fertilizers and better ones. We keep on developing better kinds of crop plants—wheat, corn, sorghum, and the like. We have learned to control the weeds that get into our croplands. And, lastly, we have learned how to use our land better.

As far as anyone can see, we can expect to go on doing better. We have thousands of scientists working to bring this about. Every year we learn more about better ways of using our land, and about better methods of managing crops. This applies not only to crop plants but to animal production as well.

There are many areas in our country where we know that production of food would be much greater if the land were more wisely used and treated. A soil conservation program has yet to be completely installed. When it exists everywhere, then the increased productivity made possible by better crop varieties, pesticides, weed control, and fertilizer use can be realized.

Electronic systems now make it possible to read depth of snow and its water content in far-away cities

Land and the rest of the world

Americans are among the most fortunate people on earth, because our high standard of living is based on a vast area of fertile and productive land.

But not all people are this fortunate. In fact, most people in other parts of the world do not have a standard of living anywhere near as high as ours. Millions of people now starve to death, or die from diseases and illnesses resulting from lack of adequate food—*every year*.

We may feel that we have a right to the abundance in which we live, but other people who have much less envy us. They feel we do not have such a right, and if they could get powerful enough to take our lands away from us, they might try to do so. They ask, "Why should some people have more food than they can use, while the rest of us starve?"

For this reason, and for humanitarian reasons, our government has done, and is doing, a great deal to help the people of other countries. This means, of course, that our lands must produce not only enough for Americans, but for millions of other human beings.

If we undertake to help the starving millions in other parts of the world by producing as much food as our lands are capable of producing, the drain on our land will be far greater than we have ever experienced. The need for expert assistance to other countries will also increase. We will need to put our scientists to work even more intensively, for we will need to know even more than we do about land use and food production.

*American engineer (right) helps Egyptians
with irrigation problems on the Nile Delta*

Design for living

As America was settled, the pattern of the land was gradually changed. The forests were cut down and the prairies were plowed up. Buffalo and antelope were replaced by cattle and sheep.

The first land pattern was wilderness. The second land pattern was a patchwork of square fields set down every which way, but without much thought for the land itself.

The modern land pattern is a better pattern. The fields no longer form squares, but fit the rounded, rolling contours of the land itself. This new pattern results from a combination of the best of everything we know about using land. Every acre is used in accordance with its own particular capability and managed according to its individual needs. The pattern will be improved because we are learning new things all the time about the soil and how to use it.

It is really only a few years since the bold new patterns began to appear on American land. They may seem strange at first, but they mean well-being and security for the people of America. They are spreading fast as, year by year, this important work goes forward.

The great soil conservation movement to protect and defend American land is a step of historic importance. As a nation we came dangerously close to ruining our greatest and most wonderful heritage—the land on which our way of life depends—but we now realize that only so long as America uses its soil with care and respect can it hope to remain a great and powerful nation.

The New Look in America

Further reading

This book doesn't tell you all there is to know about soil conservation, by any means. It is too important and too big a subject for one book. You will need to read more books about it, and you can find some good ones in your public library.

Also, if you are really interested in learning more about soil conservation, you should write to: The Soil Conservation Service, U. S. Department of Agriculture, Washington, D. C. This Service has a large number of bulletins about every phase of the subject. They have one, for example, on *Soil Erosion*. If you live near a city, they have a bulletin on *Soil Conservation at Home* that contains tips for city and suburban dwellers. If you are interested in history, there is a bulletin called *Conquest of the Land Through 7,000 Years*. There is also one on *Early American Soil Conservationists*.

There is a bulletin called *That Land Down There,* which explains the soil conservation patterns you can see from an airplane, and there is one about *Soil Conservation Districts,* which tells how they work. And there are bulletins that deal with the various conservation practices you have read about in this book. They tell you a great deal more about each one.

If you know exactly what you want, ask for it. If you do not, ask the Service to send you their list of bulletins. From this you can tell what they have, and you can decide what you need.

All these bulletins are free, and they are usually sent out by return mail.

If you would like a picture of soil conservation work in full color, in your state—or in any other, or all fifty states—you can order these from the Superintendent of Documents, Washington, D. C. Ask for the list of the *America the Beautiful* series. They will send you this, with prices, which are very low (ten cents each in 1968). These pictures are in full color and worthy of being framed and hung in your home or classroom. Each one is a reproduction of the finest color photograph yet taken of soil and water conservation scenes in each of our states.

Index

windbreaks and, 78
Soil
  burning as enemy of, 28, 56, 57
  classification of, 60
  formation of, 26
  house foundations and, 128, 129
  humus and, 28
  legumes in improvement of, 80, 81
  maps of, 58, 138
  relationship of food to, 20
  winter cover for, 86, 87
  See also Erosion; Topsoil
Soil conservation districts, 136–41
Soil Conservation Service, U.S., 138, 156
Soil profiles, 26
Soil surveys, 58, 59
Sorghum stripping, 76
South, the
  crop rotation in, 82
  erosion in, 34
  primeval forest of, 12
  winter cover in, 86
Southwest, the, 16
  agriculture in, 18
Sprinkler irrigation, 92
Storm sewers, 128
Straight furrows, 66
Stream banks, 114, 115
Strip cropping, 68, 69, 82, 100, 140
  against wind erosion, 76, 77
Stubble, 76, 88, 100
Subsoil, 26
Suburbs, 22, 128, 140
Surveyor's rod, 27
Swamps, 94, 102, 122
  primeval, 12

Terraces, 70–73
  bench, 46, 47
  of orchards, 98
  waterways from, 72, 73, 100
Texas, dust storms in, 42
Tile drains, 94, 95
Timgad, 44, 45
Topsoil
  composition of, 26
  erosion of, 30, 31, 36, 40, 43, 54, 56, 78, 86, 124

floods and, 38
  preserved by pasture, 104
Trees
  of primeval forests, 10, 12, 16
  for steep slopes, 140
  in woodland, 110, 111
  See also Forests

Utah, 106, 107

Vetch, 80, 86, 87
Vineyards, 98

Washington, George, 34, 48, 49
Watersheds, 114, 142, 147
Waterways from terraces, 72, 73, 100
Weed control, 100, 150
West, the
  agriculture in, 18
  at arrival of settlers, 16
  irrigation in, 92
  range land of, 106–9
Wheat, 18, 42, 76, 82
Wichita Refuge, 15
Wild fruits, 90, 102
Wilderness, 10–16
  reshaped by settlers, 18
Wildlife
  in American wilderness, 10, 14
  field borders and, 90
  hedges as shelter for, 74
  land for, 126, 127
  land for study of, 132, 133
  marshlands for, 122, 123
  odd areas of land and, 102
  ponds and, 116
  in woodland, 110
Wildlife refuges, 126, 132
Willows to prevent stream bank erosion, 114, 115
Wind erosion, 40–45
  hedges in control of, 74
  wind stripping in control of, 76, 77
  windbreaks in control of, 78, 79
Winter cover, 86, 87
Woodland, 110, 111
  from gullies, 120